That Bug!

by Harper McCann

SCHOLASTIC INC.

NEW YORK • TORONTO • LONDON • AUCKLAND • SYDNEY • MEXICO CITY • NEW DELHI • HONG KONG

Photographs © 2011: Alamy Images/Wildlife GmbH: 7; iStockphoto: 1 (Antagain), cover (arlindo71), 8 (Morley Read); ShutterStock, Inc.: 2 (irin-k), 5 (Sari Oneal), 3 (shenk1), 6 (Denis Vesely), 4 (Fong Kam Yee).

ISBN 978-0-545-34797-6

Cover and interior design by Holly Grundon. Photo research by Veroniqua Quinteros.

15 14 13 12 11 10   13 14 15 16 17/0

Printed in the U.S.A.   08

First printing, September 2011

ladybug

That bug has spots.

bee

That bug has stripes.

ant

That bug is black.

butterfly

That bug is white.

grasshopper

That bug is big.

flea

That bug is small.

cricket

That bug is the coolest
one of all!